Please accept this journal along with our
heartfelt sympathy for your loss. May it
in some small way help you during your
journey.— Beth and William Davis

In Loving Memory of
Kendall Paris Davis
April 18, 2001

Life Line

A Journal for Parents
Grieving a Miscarriage, Stillbirth, or Early Infant Death

Created by Joanie Reid
A Mother Grieving the Loss of Her Son

Printed in the United States of America.
First Edition: January 1994 — 5,000 copies.

ISBN: 1-878526-30-8
Library of Congress Catalog Card Number: 93-086825

For information contact:
Pineapple Press
P.O. Box 56
Mullett Lake, Michigan 49761

to the giver of this journal

When our son, Dustin, died, my sister gave me a journal. It was a simple gesture. A small act of caring.

A few months later, my mother shared a saved newspaper article that introduced me to the woman who has published this journal. My mother's gesture was also a simple one. Another small act of caring.

I have learned to treasure small acts of kindness. The simple gestures of caring demonstrated day in, day out. No pomp. No circumstance. No bells and whistles. I have learned how precious our moments are. How much they count. How quickly they are gone.

Someone you care about is grieving the death of a child, born or unborn. Please share this journal with them. Your simple act of caring may be the life line they need.

my river of grief...a personal note

Since you are reading this right now, I know you are suffering greatly. I am so sorry. So very and sincerely sorry.

I, too, have suffered deeply with the death of our unborn son, Dustin. And that, in essence, is why I have developed this journal.

Like many pregnancies, mine with Dustin was unique. In 1983, shortly after delivering our now 10-year-old daughter, Katie, I had a D & C. Muscle tissue was scraped and subsequent tests indicated my uterus had scarred together. After two surgeries to open my uterus, I was given a 50 to 60 percent chance of becoming pregnant again, with an increased risk of tubal pregnancy.

I didn't become pregnant and, in the summer of 1987, Dave and I adopted our second daughter, Kristen. The following spring, I had my right ovary and fallopian tube removed because of endometriosis.

Over time, the possibility of becoming pregnant again faded completely. We hadn't used birth control for 8 years, my uterus was scarred, I had only one ovary... Having another child wasn't something we even considered.

And then, on Halloween, 1991, we learned that I was, in fact, pregnant. My doctor used the term "remarkable." I thought "immaculate conception" might be more like it. I was overwhelmed with disbelief. And despite my attempts at humor, I was a nervous wreck.

What followed were several weeks — eventually, months — of restless, worry-filled nights and clocks that ticked way too slowly as we passed one important milestone after another. No tubal pregnancy. Normal ultrasound. No miscarriage. Strong heartbeat. Perfect development. No sign of problems with my uterus. Ten tiny little fingers and toes. It was incredible.

And then the final milestone: The amniocentesis confirmed that we had a healthy baby boy on the way. I can't begin to describe the relief I felt. This was really going to happen. We were going to have a son.

Our world began revolving around his arrival. Deciding whether to move or remodel. Agreeing and disagreeing on names. Reading the baby-sitting book Katie brought home from the library. Reassuring Kristen that not all brothers beat up their sisters. The list, as you know, is endless.

And then he died. Just like that. Unexpectedly. No warning. Just no heartbeat. I was in shock...again.

Ultimately I had surgery to take Dustin from my uterus. Inducing labor was unsuccessful in relaxing the very tight stricture that had formed which left my uterus looking much like an hour glass. Dustin was in the top half, but the amniotic sac and umbilical cord had somehow slipped to the bottom. The stricture made it impossible for him to live.

Tears ran down my cheeks as I held my lifeless son. And kissed him. And talked to him. I tried so hard to capture every detail of his tiny little features. I was so painfully aware that I would never see them again.

A few days later I left the hospital with a very heavy heart and arms that cradled only a picture and a little blue cap.

My perfect little son, in all his innocence, died because of my imperfect uterus. I, his own mother, could not protect him. My despair was overwhelming. My pain, unbearable. I thought I might drown in my own grief.

You and I have each lost a child. We're in the same river. Still, our circumstances and experiences are not the same. Perhaps you lost your child through miscarriage. Or stillbirth, as I did. Or by making the heart-wrenching decision to end your pregnancy. Perhaps your child died shortly after birth. Or while still an infant. Or... We experience this river from different canoes.

And I don't know exactly what this river is like for you. But it's been very rough for me, especially when I was first thrown in. The raging waters were merciless and relentless. I was not at all sure I would survive.

I have survived, though. Thanks in large part to the people on the river banks. Like my nurses. My doctor. My friends. And my family. I know it was hard for them to understand the depth of my pain. And it was hard for them to watch me suffer so greatly. Still, for the most part, they tried not to minimize my loss or rush me through my grief. That was important.

Reading helped me stay afloat, too. Especially the books and pamphlets and poetry written by the people who started down this river before me. My own feelings of helplessness and vulnerability were written across their pages. I realized I was not alone in the river. And that helped me survive it.

And I poured out my heart in a journal. A journal my sister had the wisdom to bring me while I was in the hospital.

I dumped all my emotions and all my confusion on paper. I wrote — without editing, without polish — about how I felt, what had happened, questions I struggled with. I wrote each entry to Dustin, the son we had just lost.

Somehow it helped. Tremendously. It helped me stay close to Dustin. It helped me survive the rough and raging waters I had suddenly been thrown into. It helped me, eventually, to navigate into calmer waters. In many ways, my sister's gift to me became my life line.

I developed this journal so you, too, would have a life line. An outlet for your grief. A way to help you remember and survive the raging waters, no matter what those waters look and feel like from your canoe.

For losing a child is a very personal experience. A very intimate experience. A very private experience. At the deepest level you must go through it alone. You are in your own canoe.

But you are not alone in this river. I'm in it, too. Hurting with you. Healing with you. Hoping with you for calmer waters.

Joanie Reid
Holland, Michigan

to those on the river banks

My child has died, and I am suffering.

I know it must be painful for you, too, to see me in my sorrow. But

Please don't rush me through my grief. My grief has a life and timetable of its own. I suspect it will always be with me.

Please don't remind me how grateful I should be for my own health. Healthy is not what I'm feeling right now.

Please don't tell me how lucky I am to have other children who are full of life. I'm not feeling very lucky. The reality of my son's death surrounds me.

Please don't tell me that I can have other children. I wanted this child. This baby. My son.

Please don't tell me that life goes on. My son's life has stopped and, momentarily, so has mine.

Please don't believe that I didn't know my son and conclude that my pain is somehow less intense...that my sorrow is temporary or shallow. I knew my son as if he were a part of me, because he was a part of me. And he affected my every waking and sleeping moment. My pain is deeper than you or I could have ever imagined.

My child has died, and I am suffering.

Tears flow down my face even as I contemplate writing on this page. I have never known an emptiness this deep, or imagined that your short life could have such a profound impact on our lives.

I can't believe you're
really gone.

I want desperately for
this not to have
happened. I just want
you back! Why can't I
make it all different?

It was — and is — so absolutely unfair that I was thrown into this wretched river. Why was it *me*? Why was it *my* child?

I am in the raging
waters. And I am
struggling.

Please, God, let this be
someone else's life.

I woke up in a panic last night. I was suddenly struck — almost physically — by the possibility that I had unwittingly done something to cause this to happen to you. The thought torments me.

I'm haunted by the fact
that I couldn't protect
you. My innocent baby.
So vulnerable.

I am trying so hard to
will this last week
away. I have spent
hours and hours
mentally rewriting
what happened. I
imagine and
reimagine. I create
scenario after
scenario. And of
course, you are always
healthy, and you
always live.

I so desperately long for relief from these raging waters. I so desperately long to get away from this torment.

I feel like I'm dreaming. I'm in the dream. And at the same time I'm standing on the outside looking in on myself. It's too unreal to be real. But it's too real to be a dream.

I am struggling.
Suffering terribly. Each
moment is saturated
with such intense grief.

This feeling of
emptiness is so intense.
Pervasive. Consuming.
I am depleted. Drained
dry. Exhausted. I am
hollow.

I never expected life to be fair. I never believed in some universal justice. But I am overwhelmed by how unfair this is. I am so intensely angry, frustrated, tormented, that I couldn't do a thing — not one damn thing — to stop this from happening.

People on the banks of this river are still going about their business. Although now they seem to move in slow motion. I'm amazed that their lives are going on as if nothing has happened.

I'm crushed by all this.
The reality that I will
never have you back is
always with me.

I am trapped in a blanket of fog. I have no idea what lies ahead or how to negotiate beyond the all-encompassing pain of this moment.

I want desperately to call my doctor and meet with him...to ask all the questions that continue to torment me. And yet, I'm afraid of my own vulnerability, my own feelings of helplessness. I'm afraid I just might ask him to put his arms around me and hold me. Maybe tomorrow.

I feel like I need to do something, but I don't know what. I'm immobilized by all of this.

I am at the mercy of
this river. I have no
control.

I didn't know emptiness could be so deep — it goes on and on and on.

I thought I was getting stronger but now I realize it's just not that easy.

I can hardly pull myself out of bed. Why should I? For what purpose? To chat? To play a game? To straighten the shoes by the back door? Everything seems so unimportant, so trivial and inconsequential.

Where have all these pregnant women come from??? They are everywhere!!!

Crying comes easily
and suddenly —
nothing in particular
seems to trigger it.

I have an ache in my stomach — a knot that doesn't go away, but gnaws at me constantly.

The thought that I'll carry this pain with me for the rest of my life is overwhelming. How do people continue to function?

People on shore assure me I will get to calmer waters, but I am not convinced. And I certainly don't know the way.

I have no idea where each bend in this river will lead. I have no idea where the bends are. I don't even know if there are bends.

Please, God, let this be over.

Others say they need
me, but I have nothing
to give. I am empty.
And so needy myself.

I want someone to hold me, and to rock me, and to tell me it will be ok. To protect me. To comfort me. I just want to surrender myself. To abandon myself. I feel such intense sorrow. And I am so vulnerable.

Sundays are the worst.
I don't know why. But
they are.

The river's currents have taken me to a part of this river that I can handle. It's not so violent here. Just a little choppy. I think the desperate struggle is finally over.

I have always known intellectually that life can be snatched away. But now, I have experienced it. It is a very different kind of learning.

Will your death make my life more purposeful? More connected? More meaningful? More integrated into a larger sense of community?

Where will this river take me?

Whatever lessons
there are to be learned
from this devastating
experience — no
matter how profound
or powerful they turn
out to be — they will
not have been worth
learning in this way.

There is no one right way to grieve. Our decisions and choices are our own.

While I was sorting my mail today, I came across a brochure from a diaper service — with my name on it. Do these reminders end?

Your death changed my life. It marked the beginning of a new perspective. A new sensitivity to the fragility of life. A new appreciation for the preciousness of each moment. I find myself cherishing even the most unspectacular moments.

I let in the very uneasy
notion that you have
more profoundly,
more fundamentally,
affected me in your
death than perhaps
you would have had
you lived.

I felt such oneness
with you. It's very hard
— impossible, perhaps
— to disconnect.
Maybe that's why
writing to you is so
soothing. It helps me
feel connected. It
softens the pain of our
separation.

Rock-a-bye baby
Rock a baby bye-bye

No gentle breeze will
   touch your face
No sand between
   your toes
No teddy bear will
   grace your arms
No...

The tears flow. My poor baby. I am so, so sorry life turned out this way for us — you and me. Others, too, but mostly you and me.

So many of my
questions haven't been
answered — so many
are unanswerable.

I learned today that a friend thought I was crying too much. That I should be beyond that by now. She can't know how devastating it is to lose a baby — I know that. Still, my heart aches when someone I care about judges me in my grief. I am already feeling so vulnerable. So wounded. Wondering, myself, if I will be ok.

For each of us, grief
has a life of its own
and a timetable of its
own.

I appreciate family
members and friends
who have not rushed
me through this, who
have given me space
even though they can
not understand how
much I need it.

My sister thought I was at a point where I could handle some humor. She sent me a card that said (outside) "They say you learn the most from your most difficult experiences." (inside) "What a stupid system."

So much pours from my heart each and every day. Tablets and sheets of paper follow me around. I scribble notes to myself about things I want to write, feelings I'm having. And I feel frustrated that I can not suspend time long enough to get it all on paper.

"Why me?" is no longer my question. I have learned to accept that this is the river I'm in and this is my canoe. "What do I do now?" "How do I respond?" have become my issues.

I went to the grocery store this afternoon. I was walking past the baby food, inwardly commenting to myself that it didn't bother me. Then I saw a pregnant woman and my eyes immediately filled.

I hear the birds again. I smell the flowers. And I try hard to remember that whatever meaning there is in life is found in each moment. How precious these moments are. How quickly they can be snatched away.

I've been thinking about endings and beginnings. There was such a tragic ending to your beginning. I have come to terms with it, though. I accept it. I have learned to live with it and move on. But I am not the same person I was before.

I am in the river, but
now the river is also in
me.

The buoys, the markers in this river, were most visible to me only after I had passed them. They showed me where I had been, not where I was going.

I sometimes look at the people I love and wish with all my heart and soul that I could suspend time and capture them forever, just as they are. I realize more fully how precious they are. I am grateful to you and your short life for that. I hope I can hold on to it.

There really aren't
endings, you know.
Although it feels like it.
Endings just flow into
new beginnings, which
flow into middles,
which flow into
endings, which flow
back into beginnings. I
believe that now, now
that I've struggled
through the reality of
your death and have
found some peace. I'm
glad no one tried to tell
me that at the time,
though. It would have
brought no comfort.

The crocuses we
planted in your
memory have
blossomed. It is
finally Spring.

reflections

Has my heart-wrenching struggle with life's most fundamental questions somehow "enriched" me? "Enriched" doesn't quite seem like the right word, but there is greater depth, certainly.

Do I more profoundly understand the fragility of life and the preciousness of each moment? There is no doubt.

Do I have greater heartfelt compassion and empathy for those I see around me who suffer in some way? Yes, I really do.

Do I feel a more profound sense of community? Of connection? Absolutely. Like thread in a tapestry, I am woven into relationships, inextricably tied to something larger than myself.

Do I realize the profound impact your short life has had on me and conclude that I, too, can have an impact on the lives of others? In my heart of hearts I know one person can make a difference.

Are these some of the lessons to be learned from your death? Is this the rainbow that follows the storm? The light at the end of the tunnel? The May flowers that follow the April showers? I suspect.

Would I exchange these lessons of death and sorrow for your life? Would I give up the rainbow, the light, the May flowers? In a heartbeat.

thank you

This journal began as a tentative thought in a vulnerable woman grieving the loss of her unborn son. It only turned into a real possibility when Molly Minnick of Pineapple Press entered the picture. From the day we met, Molly held an unwavering belief in the value of this project. Her unconditional support freed me to realize my vision: developing a journal for parents like myself. I will always be indebted to Molly for her support and enthusiasm. Without it, this journal would have remained a tentative thought in a vulnerable woman.

Asking a friend to edit a journal that has been developed from personal, intimate writings is no small request. Yet that is exactly what I asked of my friend Lois Maassen. Lois is one of those rare individuals who have the ability to share their expertise with sensitivity, warmth, humor, and clarity. Her caring and her insights were invaluable. No one else could have done what she did.

Nancy Vanderboom-Lausch designed the artwork for this journal. Her ability to envision many possibilities was a true source of energy when I felt burdened by my limited thinking. I am deeply grateful for her creative talent and her commitment to capturing the essence of my feelings and experiences and translating them into graphic form.